TEST FOR UNIT 2 OF *LATIN: LEVEL ONE*

1) Write the Latin vowel which your teacher says:_____ .

2) Write another Latin vowel which your teacher says:_____ .

3) Write another Latin vowel which your teacher says:_____ .

4) Write the Latin syllable which your teacher says:_____ .

5) Write another Latin syllable which your teacher says:_____ .

6) Write another Latin syllable which your teacher says:_____ .

7) Read this sentence aloud to your teacher: **Vestis virum reddit.**

TEST FOR UNIT 3 OF *LATIN: LEVEL ONE*

Write the Latin vowels which your teacher will pronounce. Remember: if the vowel is *long* you must add the macron.

1) This vowel is _____ .

2) This vowel is _____ .

3) This vowel is _____ .

4) This vowel is _____ .

5) This vowel is _____ .

6) Read aloud the Basic Sentence which your teacher indicates:

>   **Manus manum lavat.**
>
>   **Hilarem datōrem dīligit Deus.**
>
>   **Vēritātem diēs aperit.**

TEST FOR UNIT 4 OF *LATIN: LEVEL ONE*

1) Write the Basic Sentence which each of these pictures illustrates.
   Be sure to mark the long vowels with macrons.

   a) **El· · · · · · · ·   n· ·   c· · · ·   m· · · · ·**

   _____ .

   b) **H· · · · · ·   d· · · · · ·   d· · · · · ·   D· · · ·**

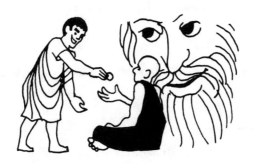

   _____ .

   c) **M· · · ·   m· · · ·   l· · · · ·**

   _____ .

2) In the sentence **Vēritātem diēs aperit**, the

subject is the word _____ ; the

object is the word _____ ; and the

verb is the word _____ .

3) Underline the *subject* in these English sentences:
   a) The smoke went up the chimney.
   b) The mouse was caught by the cat.

4) Underline the *object* in these English sentences:
   a) The woman lost her cat in the woods.
   b) The man threw his alarm clock out the window.

5) Underline the *verb* in these English sentences:
   a) The boy read his book.
   b) The stream flows quietly.

6) You were told that the most important frame of the course was one in which you learned that Latin *never* signals subject and object by the position of the words but by using the signals

   { ____ } and { ____ }.

7) Write these vowels from dictation. There will be both long and short vowels.

   a) _____ b) _____ c) _____ d) _____

8) Write these syllables from dictation. There will be both long and short vowels.

   a) _____ b) _____ c) _____ d) _____

TEST FOR UNIT 5 OF *LATIN: LEVEL ONE*

1) On the model of **Elephantus nōn capit mūrem**, describe these pictures to say that the important one ignores the unimportant one.

a) _____.

b) _____.

c) _____.

2) Underline the subject forms which have the variant signal zero:

anus	aquila	sīmia	equus	canis
aper	leō	īnfāns	taurus	vīpera
musca	piscis	lupus	rāna	asinus

3) Now describe these new situations:
   a) **Aq**- - - - **p**- - - - - **cap**- - .

_____ .

   b) **C**- - - - **s**- - - - - **dīl**- - - - .

_____ .

   c) **Ī**- - - - - **e**- - - - **mor**- - - - .

_____ .

4) Write the Basic Sentences:
   a) **L**- - - - **n**- - **m**- - - - - **l**- - - - .

_____ .

b) **V - - - - - -   n - - - - - -   p - - - - .**

_____.

5) Here are some review Basic Sentences:
   a) **H - - - - - -   d - - - - - -   d - - - - - -   D - - - .**

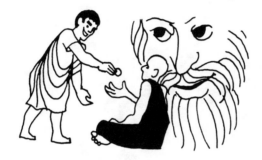

_____.

b) **M - - - -   m - - - -   l - - - - .**

_____.

6) Pronounce this Basic Sentence:
   Elephantus nōn capit mūrem.

1) **Mūrem metuit canis** best describes picture

   _____ (A/B/C/D).

2) **Aprum canis quaerit** best describes picture

   _____ (A/B/C/D).

3) Underline the words which can normally fill the adjective slot in the sentence below.

   The { walked, happy, was, this, quickly, John, cold } man came into the room.

4) Underline the words which can normally fill the adjective slot in the sentence below.

   The man seems { fat. goes. gently. thing. bright. stupid. radio. }

5) In the sentence "The small boy sees the dog" we know that the boy is the one which is small. We know this because of the

   _____ of the word "small" in the sentence.

6) Draw a line under the *adjective* in each of these sentences:
   a) **Cautus metuit foveam lupus.**
   b) **Nōn semper aurem facilem habet Fēlīcitās.**

7) Underline the word which receives the most emphasis from its *position*.
Elephantus nōn capit mūrem.

8) Write these Basic Sentences:
a) **L · · · · n · · m · · · · · l · · · · .**

_____.

b) **V · · · · · · n · · · · · · p · · · · .**

_____.

c) **V · · · · · v · · · · r · · · · · · .**

_____.

Remember to mark the long quantities.

9) Write this Basic Sentence from dictation:

    _____

    _____ .

10) Pronounce this Basic Sentence:
    Cautus metuit foveam lupus.

TEST FOR UNIT 7 OF *LATIN: LEVEL ONE*

1) Write the Basic Sentences. Remember to mark the long quantities.

a) **Et··· c······· ūn·· h···· u····· s····.**

_____

_____ .

b) **N·· qu····· a···· m····· ēl········.**

_____

_____ .

?) nderline just the kernel of the Basic Sentence and label with **- s, - m, - t** where appropriate.

a) **Cautus metuit foveam lupus.**

b) **Vēritās numquam perit.**

3) Answer these questions on Basic Sentences. Remember that the answer must be in the *same case* as the question word.

a) **Quem vestis reddit?** _____ .

b) **Quis nōn semper habet aurem facilem?**

_____ .

c)   **Quem lupus nōn mordet?** _____ .

d)   **Quem nōn capit elephantus?** _____ .

e)   **Quem Deus dīligit?** _____ .
     (Two-word answer required)

4)   Write these Basic Sentences:
a)   **V - - - - -   v - - - -   r - - - - - .**

_____ .

b)   **N - -   s - - - - -   aur - -   f - - - - - -   h - - - -**
     F - - - - - - - - .

_____

_____ .

c)   **V - - - - - - - -   d - - -   ap - - - - - .**

_____ .

TEST FOR UNIT 8 OF *LATIN: LEVEL ONE*

1) Write these new Basic Sentences, remembering to put in all the macrons:

   a)   **L··   v····   īr····,   īr····   l····   n··**
       v·····.

_____

_____.

   b)   **V·····   v···   fr·····,   l····   ag···,**
       f·····   l······.

_____

_____.

   c)   **D···   n··   pr····,   d···   n······.**

_____

_____.

d) P····· n·· s····· av·······
s·· ir·····.

_____

_____.

2) Answer these questions on the new Basic Sentences. Remember to give the answer in the proper case.

a) **Quem fūr cognōscit?** _____.

b) **Quis lupum cognōscit?** _____.

c) **Quis vītam nōn regit?** _____.

3) Expand the sentences with the missing elements to make both kernels complete, as in the sample below.

Sample: **Piscem piscis cognōscit et rāna rānam.** ⟶
Piscem piscis cognōscit et rāna rānam cognōscit.

a) **Taurum lupus metuit, lupum taurus.** ⟶

Taurum lupus metuit, lupum taurus

_____.

b) **Canis sīmiam nōn metuit sed dīligit.** ⟶

Canis sīmiam nōn metuit sed _____

_____ **dīligit.**

c) **Pecūniam quaerit fūr, nōn aeger.** ⟶

Pecūniam quaerit fūr, nōn _____

_____ **aeger.**

4) Write the review Basic Sentences:

a) **Et··· c······· ū··· h···· um····**
   s····.

_____

_____ .

b) **N·· qu····· ae··· m······ ēl········**

_____

_____ .

c) **N·· s····· au··· f······ h····**
   F·········.

_____

_____ .

5) Ask the question which calls for the underlined word in these review Basic Sentences.

a) **Vestis _virum_ reddit.**

_____?

b) **Crūdēlem medicum _intemperāns aeger_ facit.**

_____?

c) **Elephantus nōn capit _mūrem._**

_____?

1) Choose your answer from these words, putting it in the same
    case as the question word: **juvenis, taurus, fēmina, īnfāns,
    mūs, canis, vulpēs, leō, equus.** Remember the macrons.

    a) **Cum quō currit taurus?**

        Cum _____.

    b) **Cum quō fēmina est?**

        Cum _____.

    c) **Cum quō mūs est?**

        Cum _____.

d) **Cum quō vulpēs est?**

Cum _____.

e) **Cum quō equus est?**

Cum _____.

2) Complete the paradigms:

		a)	b)	c)
nominative:		**rāna**	**Deus**	**fraus**
accusative:		_____	_____	_____
ablative:		_____	_____	_____

3) Write the new Basic Sentence.
N - - - - av - - - - - - s - - - p - - - - - - - -.

_____ .

4) And, as usual, there is a Basic Sentence review.

a) **L·· v···· īr····, īr···· l····**
   n·· v····.

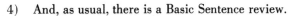

_____

_____ .

b) **F···· f·· c········ et l···· l····.**

_____

_____ .

c) **V····· v··· fr·····, l···· ag···,**
   f····· l·····.

_____

_____

_____ .

d) V···· r···· F······, n·· S········.

_____

_____ .

1) Answer the questions by writing out the whole words. Remember macrons and proper case.

   a) **Quō locō taurus est?**
      I - l - - - .

    _____ _____ .

   b) **Sub quō locō est canis?**
      S - - gr - - - .

    _____ _____ .

   c) **Cum quō est fēmina?**
      C - - ef - - - - - .

    _____ _____ .

2) Write the accusative and ablative of the following nouns:

a) **musca** _____

_____

_____

b) **asinus** _____

_____

_____

c) **laus** _____

_____

_____

d) **quercus** _____

_____

_____

e) **faciēs** _____

_____

_____

f) **umbra** _____

_____

_____

g) **saccus** _____

_____

_____

h) **vulpēs** _____

_____

_____

i) **anus** _____

_____

_____

j) **aciēs** _____

_____

_____

3) Write the accusative and ablative of the following adjectives:

a) **hilaris** _____

_____

_____

b) **cautus** _____

_____

_____

c) **parva** _____

_____

_____

d) **intemperāns** _____

_____

_____

4) Answer these questions on the new Basic Sentences:
   a) **"Quō parva vīpera spatiōsum taurum necat?"**

   " _____ ."

   b) **"Sub quō est līs?"**

   " _____ ."

5) Write these Basic Sentences:

a) **Cr · · · · · ·   m · · · · · ·   in · · · · · · · · ·**
   aeg · ·   f · · · · .

_____

_____ .

b) **D · · ·   n · ·   pr · · · · ·,   d · · ·   n · · · · · .**

_____

_____ .

c) **P · · · · · ·   n · ·   s · · · · ·   av · · · · · · ·**
   s · ·   ir · · · · · .

_____

_____ .

d) N· · · · av· · · · · · s· · · p· · · · · · · .

_____

_____ .

TEST FOR UNIT 11 OF *LATIN: LEVEL ONE*

1) Give short answers to the questions on this picture:

   a)   **Quem īnfāns irrītat?**

       _____.

   b)   **Ā quō īnfāns nōn dīligitur?**

       Ā _____.

   c)   **Ā quō sīmia irrītātur?**

       Ab_____.

   d)   **Quem sīmia nōn dīligit?**

       _____.

2) Give short answers to the questions on this picture:

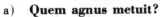

   a)   **Quem agnus metuit?**

       _____.

   b)   **Quem aquila capit?**

       _____.

   c)   **Ā quō agnus capitur?**

       Ab _____.

   d)   **Ā quō aquila nōn premitur?**

       Ab _____.

3) Write the accusative and ablative of the adjective-noun combinations which follow:

a) **crūdēlis medicus** _____

b) **canis magnus** _____

_____   _____

_____   _____

4) Underline the one word which receives the most emphasis from its position:
Vulpēs vult fraudem, lupus agnum, fēmina laudem.

5) Transform these sentences from active to passive.

a) **Vir fēminam quaerit.** ⟶
Ā ---- ------ -----itur.

Ā _____ .

b) **Anus juvenem tenet.** ⟶
Ab --- ------- ---ētur.

Ab _____ .

c) **Piscis vīperam mordet.** ⟶
Ā ----- ------ ----ētur.

Ā _____ .

6) These questions are on a new Basic Sentence:

a) **Quem canis parvus saepe tenet?** _____ .

b) **Ā quō aper magnus saepe capitur? Ā** _____

_____ .

7) Answer these questions on familiar Basic Sentences. The answers all require a transformation of the original word. Remember that the answer must be in the same case as the question word and have all the long quantities marked by macrons.

a) **Ā quō spatiōsus taurus morsū necātur?**

Ā _____ .

b) **Ā quō vīta regitur? Ā** _____ .

c) **Quis ab elephantō nōn capitur?** _____ .

1) Write the paradigms of these nouns:

    a) **vitium** _____   b) **opus** _____

       _____   _____

       _____   _____

    c) **auctor** _____

       _____

       _____

2) Write the new Basic Sentences illustrated by these pictures:

    a) **S - - - - - - - -   v - - -   ob - - - - - - - - - .**

    _____.

    b) **N - - - - - -   p - - - - ' - - -   s - - -**
         p - - - - ' - -   v - - - - - - - .

    _____

    _____.

c) **M**··· **r**····· **b**··· **p**·······.

_____ .

3) Answer these questions on the new Basic Sentences:
a) **Sine quō est nēmō?**

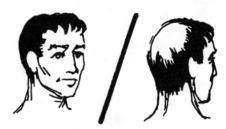

Sine_____ .

b) **Quid ab auctōre laudātur?**

_____ .

4) Answer these questions on review Basic Sentences:
a) **Quid numquam perit?**

_____ .

b) **Quid fēmina vult?**

_____.

c) **Quālem medicum facit intemperāns aeger?**

_____.

d) **Quālem aurem nōn semper habet Fēlīcitās?**

_____.

e) **Quid agit parva vīpera?**

_____
(Two-word answer satisfactory)

TEST FOR UNIT 13 OF *LATIN: LEVEL ONE*

1) Answer these questions on the new Basic Sentences:
   a) **Ā quō dōnātur et genus et forma?**

   Ā _____ .
   (Two-word answer required)

   b) **Quid ab īnsānō mediō flūmine quaeritur?**

   _____ .

   c) **Quālem aquam habet fōns impūrus?**

   _____ .
   (Is each answer in the same case as its question word?)

2) Give the paradigms of these noun-adjective combinations:

a) **magnum opus** _____

_____

_____

b) **canis magnus** _____

_____

_____

c) **leō parvus** _____

_____

_____

d) **hilare dictum** _____

_____

_____

e) **īrātus fūr** _____

_____

_____

f) **crūdēlis spēs** _____

_____

_____

g) **facile genus** _____

_____

_____

h) **magnus lacus** _____

_____

_____

i) **blanda ōrātiō** _____

_____

_____

j) **medium flūmen** _____

_____

_____

3) Give the new Basic Sentences which these pictures illustrate:
   a) **M** - - -   **s** - - -   - -   **c** - - - - - -   **s** - - - .

_____

_____

b) **R·· nōn sp··, f····· nōn d·····,
qu····· am····.**

_____

_____

_____ .

c) **H···· s··· v······ bl···· ōr····· .**

_____

_____ .

4) Give these review Basic Sentences:
a) **S·· j····· l·· ··t.**

_____ .

b) Ā c··· nōn m···· s···· t····· a···.

Ā _____

_____ .

c) L·· v···· īr····, īr···· l···· nōn v····.

_____

_____ .

TEST FOR UNIT 14 OF *LATIN: LEVEL ONE*

1) Complete the description of the following pictures:
   a) **Jūd·· cum fēm···· lītem ha····.**

_____

_____ .

   b) **Vīn·· ā sīm··· b···tur.**

_____ .

2) Answer the questions on these pictures:
   a) **Quī aquam bibunt?**

_____ .

b) **Quōs metuit fēmina?**

_____.

c) **Quī ā vulpe inveniuntur?**

_____

d) **Quōs mūs irrītat?**

_____.

3) Write the paradigms of these nouns:

a) **rāna** _____   b) **taurus** _____

_____ _____   _____ _____

_____ _____   _____ _____

c) **aper** _____

_____ _____

_____ _____

4) Write the new Basic Sentence illustrated by this picture:

M - - - - - - c - - - - - - f - - - - - v - - - - - v - - - - .

_____

_____ .

5) Answer these questions on the new Basic Sentences:
   a) **Quō dī coluntur?**

_____ .

   b) **Ā quō muscae nōn capiuntur?**

Ab _____ .

   c) **Quem lacrimae pāscunt?**

_____ .

6) Write the following review Basic Sentences:
   a) **D··· n·· pr····, d··· n·····.**

   _____

   _____ .

   b) **S········ v··· ob·········.**

   _____

   _____ .

   c) **Īn····· m···· fl····· qu····· aqu···.**

   _____

   _____ .

d) **H**···· **s**··· **v**······ **bl**···· **ōr**····· .

_____

_____ .

1) Answer these questions on the following pictures:

a) **Quem anūs cūrant?** _____

_____.

b) **Ā quibus aeger cūrātur?   Ab** _____.

c) **Quōs sīmia pāscit?** _____.

d) **Ā quō īnfantēs pāscuntur?   Ā** _____.

e) **Quid fūrēs tenent?** _____.

f) **Ā quibus saccus tenētur?   Ā** _____.

2) Fill in the missing blanks in order to describe these pictures:

a) Īnf - - - - - sīm - - - pāscunt.

_____.

b) T - - - - sub qu - - - - - - s stant.

_____.

c) Juv - - - - stultus arc - - suōs lavat.

_____

_____.

3) Decline in the singular and the plural.

a) **fovea** _____ _____

_____ _____ _____ _____

_____ _____ _____ _____

b) **agnus** _____

c) **auctor** _____ d) **saltus** _____

_____ _____ _____ _____

_____ _____ _____ _____

e) **rēs** _____

_____ _____

_____ _____

4) In Latin we tell which noun an adjective modifies by the fact

that the adjective is in the same _____, _____,

and _____ as the noun with which it agrees.

5) Decline the following noun-plus-adjective combinations. Remember, it is possible that the adjective is not in the same declension as the noun.

a) **fōns pūrus** _____ _____

_____ _____

_____ _____

b) **blanda ōrātiō** _____ _____

_____ _____

_____ _____

6) Underline the nouns in this list which are *nominative* case:
   **imitātiō, taurō, nēmō, ōrātiō,
   equō, saccō, lupō, vitiō**

7) Underline the nouns in this list which are *nominative* case:
   **muscās, foveās, vēritās,
   poenās, lacrimās, fēlīcitās**

8) Write the new Basic Sentences which these pictures illustrate:
   a) **P - - - - D - - -, n - - pl - - - -, asp - - - - m - - - -.**

   _____

   _____ .

   b) **- - au - - - - - c - - - - - - - - - as - - - - .**

   _____ .

9) Answer the questions on these new Basic Sentences:
   Stultī timent Fortūnam, sapientēs ferunt.

   a) **Ā quibus Fortūna timētur?** _____ **Ā** _____ .

   Fortūna fortēs metuit, īgnāvōs premit.

   b) **Quī ā Fortūnā premuntur?** _____ .

10) Write the review Basic Sentences which these pictures illustrate:
    a) **M - - - s - - - - - c - - - - - - s - - -.**

    _____ .

b) **C**···· **m**···· **f**···· **l**····.

_____

_____.

c) **Cr**······ **l**······· **p**·······,
n·· **fr**········.

_____

_____.

d) **N**··· **s**··· **v**···· ····.

_____.

TEST FOR UNIT 16 OF *LATIN: LEVEL ONE*

1) Write the paradigms of the following nouns; be sure to observe which are neuter.

a) **rēgnum** _____ _____   b) **genus** _____ _____

_____ _____   _____ _____

_____ _____   _____ _____

c) **capillus** _____ _____   d) **mūs** _____ _____

_____ _____   _____ _____

_____ _____ _____   _____ _____ _____

2) Change the underlined words from singular to plural.

a) **Sine factō: Sine** _____ .

b) **Ex opere: Ex** _____ .

c) **Vir vitium habet: Vir** _____ **habet.**

d) **Flūmen ab īnsānō quaeritur:**

_____ **ab īnsānō quaeruntur.**

3) Underline the words which are the ambiguous nominative-accusative plural neuter:
Fortūna Fāta rēgīna aqua respōnsa rēgna vīta

4) Write the new Basic Sentences which these pictures illustrate:
a) **M - - - - - - c - - - - - , p - - - - n - - - - - - - - .**

_____

_____ .

b) **P**···· **l**···· **c**······ **an**····.

_____

_____.

5) Answer these questions on the new Basic Sentences:

a) **Ā quibus nōlēns trahitur, volēns dūcitur?**

   Ā _____.

b) **Quem Fāta trahunt?**

   _____.

c) **Quālibus lēgibus regunt Fāta orbem?**

   _____.

d) **Quālēs lēgēs habent Fāta, certās an incertās?**

   _____.

6) Answer these questions on review Basic Sentences:
   Vestis virum reddit.

   a) **Ex quō cognōscitur vir? Ex** _____ .

   Parva necat morsū spatiōsum vīpera taurum.

   b) **Quae animālia vīperās parvās saepe metuunt?**

   _____ .

   Auctor opus laudat.

   c) **Ā quibus sua opera laudantur?**

   Ab _____ .

   Ex auribus cognōscitur asinus.

   d) **Quae membra possidet asinus stultus?**

   _____ .

   Religiō deōs colit, superstitiō violat.

   e) **Ā quibus religiō laudātur? Ā** _____ .

EXTRA READINGS*
Here are some sentences which you have never seen before. Explain
what they mean. You will notice that in the first sentence *every word
is unknown*. But this is not an impossible problem. Every word has
an English derivative. Underlined words are those which have not
yet appeared in *Latin: Level One*.

   a) **Vertit lympha rotam, rota petram,**

   petra farīnam. Med.

   _____

   _____

   _____ .

   b) **Līs lītem generat.** Anon.

   _____

   _____ .

TEST FOR UNIT 17 OF *LATIN: LEVEL ONE*

1) Answer these new questions on pictures which occurred in this
   Unit.

   a) **Quid hī fortēs ducēs regunt?**

   _____ .

   b) **Quod animal juvenis in manibus tenet?**

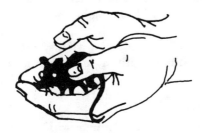

   _____ .

   c) **Ā quibus animālibus aqua bibitur?**

   Ab _____ .

2) Write the paradigms of the following words. Notice that you are
   told to what declension each word belongs.

	1st			2d	
a)	**īra**	_____	b)	**animus**	_____
	_____	_____		_____	_____
	_____	_____		_____	_____

	2d neuter			3d	

c) **vitium** _____   d) **īnfāns** _____

_____ _____   _____ _____

_____ _____   _____ _____

	3d neuter			5th	

e) **genus** _____   f) **diēs** _____

_____ _____   _____ _____

_____ _____   _____ _____

3) This will show whether you know how to figure out the meaning of new Latin words from their stems and suffixes, or from their English derivatives. Choose the word to complete the sentences from this list:

āctiō, rēs, virtūs, locus
animal, vitium, membrum, homō

a) **"Quid est neglegentia?" "** _____ **est."**

b) **"Quid est Forum Rōmānum?" "** _____ **est."**

c) **"Quid est gladiātor?" "** _____ **est."**

4) Write the new Basic Sentences which these pictures illustrate:
a) **V · · · v · · · · · · t.**

_____ .

b) **F · · · · b · · · · fr · · · · · · · t.**

_____ .

5) Answer these new questions on the new Basic Sentences:

   a) **Quibus membrīs juvenēs amantēs dūcuntur?**

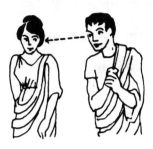

      _____ .

   b) **Quālibus cōnsiliīs regit Deus orbem?**

      Cōnsiliīs jūst_____ , fort_____ , pat_____ .

   c) **Quantam vītam habet homō?**

      _____ .

6) Answer these questions on Review Basic Sentences. Remember, the answer *must* be in the same case as the question word.
   Pūrās Deus, nōn plēnās, aspicit manūs.

   a) **Quālibus manibus Deus colitur?**

      Manibus_____ .

Lupus nōn mordet lupum.

b) **Quae animālia lupī dīligunt?** _____ .

Crūdēlem medicum intemperāns aeger facit.

c) **Quī ab intemperantibus aegrīs saepe irrītantur?**

_____ .

(Two-word answer required)

EXTRA READINGS
Underlined words are those which have not yet appeared in _Latin: Level One_. Explain the meaning of the following new sentences:

a) **Fāmam cūrant multī, paucī cōnscientiam.** Pseudo-Publilius Syrus

_____

_____

_____ .

b) **Deōs nēmō sānus timet.** Seneca, _Dē Ben._ 4.19.1

_____

_____ .

1)   Answer each question. Remember that the answer must be in the same case as the question word.

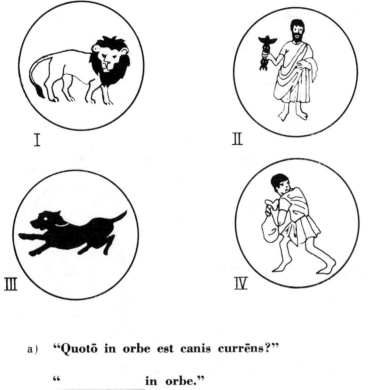

I   II   III   IV

a)   **"Quotō in orbe est canis currēns?"**

   "_____ in orbe."

b)   **Quotō in orbe est fūr?"**

   "_____ in orbe."

c)   **Quotō in orbe est leō?"**

   "_____ in orbe."

d)   **Quotō in orbe est medicus?"**

   "_____ in orbe."

2)   Write the paradigms of the following nouns:

   1st   2d

a) **rāna** _____ _____   b) **taurus** _____

   _____ _____   _____ _____

   _____ _____   _____ _____

c) **rēgnum** _____   _____   d) **mūs** _____   _____

_____   _____   _____   _____

_____   _____   _____   _____

e) **flūmen** _____   _____   f) **quercus** _____

_____   _____   _____

_____   _____   _____

5th

g) **rēs** _____   _____

_____   _____

_____   _____

3) Answer these questions on technical terms:

a) The form **lītigāns** is called a _____ .

b) **Inventus** is the past participle of the verb _____ .

c) The **in-** part of the word **incertus** is called a _____ .

d) The **-tās** part of **crūdēlitās** is called a _____ .

4) Here you can show that you know how to figure out the meaning
    of new Latin words from their stem and suffix.

a) **"Estne 'crūdēlitās' vitium an homō?"**

    " _____ ."

b) **"Estne 'amātor' āctiō an homō?"**

    " _____ ."

c) **"Estne 'jūstitia' virtūs an locus?"**

    " _____ ."

5) **w_** the new Basic Sentences which these pictures illustrate.
    a) -- v------ p----- --t v--- f--------.

_____

_____ .

b) **Thāis** h---- n-----, n----- **Laecānia**
        d-----,
        Qu-- r---- e--? **Ēm----** h--- h----,
        i--- s----.

_____

_____

_____ .

6) Write the review Basic Sentences which these pictures illustrate:
    a) **N------** p----'--- s--- p----'--
        v--------.

_____

_____ .

b) **Cr- - - - - r - - a - - - - - -.**

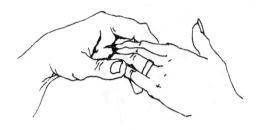

_____

_____ .

c) **Et g- - - - - - f - - - - - R- - - - - P- - - - - -
d - - - - .**

Et _____

_____ .

EXTRA READINGS
Underlined words are those which have not yet appeared in _Latin: Level One_.

7) Explain the meaning of the following new sentences:

   a) **<u>Mulierem</u> <u>ōrnat</u> <u>silentium</u>.** Translation of Sophocles

_____ .

   b) **Rēs amīcōs invenit.** Anon.

_____ .

1) Construct the paradigm of these nouns which you have never seen. Notice that you are given two of the six forms and that you are also told to what declension each noun belongs.

           1st   2d

a) **patria**   **patriae**   b) **dominus**   _____

   _____   _____   **dominum**   _____

   _____   _____   _____   _____

         2d neuter   3d

c) **exemplum**   _____   d) **rēx**   _____

   _____   _____   _____   _____

   _____   **exemplīs**   **rēge**   _____

         3d neuter   4th

e) **tempus**   _____   f) _____   **vultūs**

   _____   **tempora**   **vultum**   _____

   _____   _____   _____   _____

         5th

g) **fidēs** (no plural)

   fidem

   _____

2) Underline the verb or verbs which will fit into the pattern:

a) **Muscās leōnēs nōn** $\begin{cases} \textbf{premunt.} \\ \textbf{capiuntur.} \\ \textbf{sunt.} \\ \textbf{currunt.} \end{cases}$

b) **Vir orbēs** $\begin{cases} \textbf{vident.} \\ \textbf{scrībuntur.} \\ \textbf{indicat.} \\ \textbf{laudant.} \end{cases}$

c) **Leōnēs animālia** $\begin{cases} \textbf{necant.} \\ \textbf{sunt.} \\ \textbf{metuit.} \\ \textbf{dīliguntur.} \end{cases}$

3) Answer these questions, using the new adverb forms:

a) **"Quāliter virī hilarēs cēnant?"**

   " _____ .''

b) **Quāliter medicus cautus aegrum cūrat?"**

   " _____ .''

c) **"Quāliter Deus jūstus orbem regit?"**

   " _____ .''

4) Give an English translation of these sentences which contain relative clauses. Be careful with the relative pronouns which are in the accusative case.
   a) **Aprum, quem canis tenet, vir metuit.** =

   _____

   _____ .

   b) **Fortūna, ā quā fortēs adjuvantur, īgnāvōs neglegit.** =

   _____

   _____

   _____ .

   c) **Intemperantia, quae aegrum laedit, vitium est.** =

   _____

   _____ .

5) Make one sentence out of each pair by substituting the right form of the relative pronoun for the underlined word:
   a) **Mulier bella est; mulier laudem vult.**
      M · · · · · ,   qu · ·   l · · · · ·   v · · · ,   b · · · ·   · · t.

   _____

   _____ .

b) **Jūdex innocentem absolvit; jūdicem omnēs
jūstē laudant.**
**J - - - -, qu - - om - - - j - - - - l - - - - - -,
in - - - - - - - - abs - - - - - -.**

_____

_____ .

6) Answer this new question on the new Basic Sentence:
"Quōcum cēnat Caeciliānus?"

" _____ ."

(Several possible answers; write just one.)

7) Write the new Basic Sentence which this picture illustrates:
**N - - - - qu - - - - fl - - - - - m - - - - - - - in m - - -
p - - - - - - - - - .**

_____

_____

_____ .

8) Call these people, using the new calling form:

Mārcus. _____ ! Titus. _____ , !

9) Answer these questions on the following review Basic Sentence:
Īra furor brevis est.

a) **"Quālis est homō quī īrātus est?"**
"Īns - - - - - - t."

_____

b) **"Quid est animal quod muscās nōn quaerit?"**

_____ .

Latin: Level One Test for Unit Nineteen/65

10) Write the review Basic Sentences which these pictures illustrate:

a) **Oc··· s··· ·· am··· d····.**

b) **Ā f···· p··· p··· dē···· a···.**

Ā

EXTRA READINGS
Underlined words are those which have not yet appeared in *Latin: Level One*. Explain the meaning of the following new sentences:

a) **Piscēs magnī parvulōs comedunt.** Anon.

b) **Nōn convalēscit planta quae saepe trānsfertur.**
Seneca, *Ep.* 2.3

TEST FOR UNIT 20 OF *LATIN: LEVEL ONE*

1) Answer these questions on these pictures:

a) **"Cui anus similis est?"** **"**_____**."**

b) **"Cui vīta brevis est?"** **"**_____**."**

c) **"Cui aper pulcher vidētur?"** **"**_____**."**

2) Write just the *singular* paradigm of the following words, including the four cases you now know:

a) **patria** _____   b) **beneficium** _____   c) **mors** _____

_____   _____   _____

_____   _____   _____

_____   _____   _____

d) __manus__   e) __faciēs__

_____   _____

_____   _____

_____   _____

3) Answer this question on a new Basic Sentence:

   "Ā quō asinus laudātur?"   "Ab _____."

4) Write the new Basic Sentence which this picture illustrates:
   M··· īn······ f····, j····· ac····,
   n···· s··· s···.

   _____

   _____ .

5) Write the review Basic Sentences which these pictures illustrate:
   a) Thāis h···· n·····, n····· Laecānia
          d·····.
      Quae r···· ··t? Ēm···· h··· h····,
       i··· s··s.

   _____

   _____

   _____ .

b) **M**···· **d**· **c**·····, **p**···· **n**········.

_____
_____.

c) **In** **v**······ **p**····· ··**t** **v**··· **f**········.

_____
_____.

EXTRA READINGS

Underlined words are those which have not yet appeared in _Latin: Level One_. Explain the meaning of the following new sentences:

a) **Canis sine dentibus lātrat.** Ennius (quoted by Varro, _Dē Ling. Lat._)

_____
_____.

b) **Dōnum forma breve est.** Nemesiānus, _Ecl._ 14.24

_____
_____.

TEST FOR UNIT 21 OF *LATIN: LEVEL ONE*

1) Say that these animals are near other animals or near places. Be
    sure to notice whether the situation calls for singular or plural.

    a) **C · · · ·   pr · · · · us   l · · · · · · ·   · · t.**

    _____

    _____ .

    b) **T · · · · ·   pr · · · · · s   qu · · · · ·   · · t.**

    _____

    _____ .

    c) **M · ·   pr · · · · · s   ef · · · · · ·   · · · · .**

    _____

    _____ .

Latin: Level One Test for Unit Twenty-one/71

2) Write the four cases, singular and plural, of these nouns:

a) **vīpera** _____ _____   b) **agnus** _____ _____

_____ _____   _____ _____

_____ _____   _____ _____

_____ _____   _____ _____

c) **auctor** _____   d) **anus** _____ _____

_____ _____   _____ _____

_____ _____   _____ _____

_____ _____   _____ _____

3) Change the underlined ambiguous dative-ablative plural forms to the singular:

a) **Nōn cēnat sine aprīs Caeciliānus.** ⟶

    Nōn cēnat sine _____ Caeciliānus.

b) **Mors juvenibus nōn placet.** ⟶

    Mors _____ nōn placet.

c) **Fēmina vīnum aegrīs dat.** ⟶

    Fēmina vīnum _____ dat.

d) **Puellae mulieribus serviunt.** ⟶

    Puellae _____ serviunt.

4) Answer these questions on the new Basic Sentences:
Impōnit fīnem sapiēns et rēbus honestīs.

a) **"Quālēs rēs ā sapiente temperanter coluntur?"**

    "Etiam rēs _____ ."

Nēmō līber est quī corporī servit.

b) **"Quō regitur quī nimis vīnum bibit?"**

    " _____ suō."

5) Write the Basic Sentence, which this picture describes, about women who marry often.

Mul - - -   qu - -   mul - - -   nūb - -   mul - - -   n - - pl - - - - - .

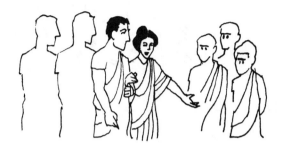

_____

_____ .

6) Answer these questions on review Basic Sentences:

Fāta regunt orbem; certā stant omnia lēge.

a) **"Cui imperant Fāta?"**

   " _____ . "

Religiō deōs colit, superstitiō violat.

b) **"Quibus nocet superstitiō?"**

   " _____ . "

7) Write the review Basic Sentences which these pictures describe:

a) **Aqu - - -   n - -   cap - -   mus - - - .**

_____

_____ .

b) **Oc··· s··· in am··· duc··**

_____ .

EXTRA READINGS
Underlined words are those which have not yet appeared in _Latin: Level One._

   a) **Lupus est homō hominī, nōn homō.** Plautus, _Asin._ 495

_____
_____ .

   b) **Gaudēns gaudentī, flēns flentī, pauper egentī, prūdēns prūdentī, stultus placet īnsipientī.** Med.

_____
_____
_____
_____ .

TEST FOR UNIT 22 OF *LATIN: LEVEL ONE*

1) Answer these questions, similar to those in the Unit:
   a) **"Estne lingua tōta faciēs?"**
      "M - - - - ē; lingua est p - - - f - - - - - .

      _____ .

   b) **"Anus rānam adjuvat. Cujus auxiliō ergō rāna adjuvātur?"**
      " - - - - auxiliō."

      _____ .

   c) **"Sī fēmina perit, cujus mors est?"**
      " - - - - - - - mors est."

      _____ .

   d) **"Sī taurus vincit, cujus victōria est?"**
      " - - - - - victōria est."

      _____ .

2) Write the *singular* paradigm (all five cases) of the following nouns:

   a) **sīmia**   b) **exemplum**   c) **vir**

      _____   _____   _____

      _____   _____   _____

      _____   _____   _____

      _____   _____   _____

   d) **canis**   e) **quercus**   f) **diēs**

      _____   _____   _____

      _____   _____   _____

      _____   _____   _____

3) **"In hāc sententiā 'Exemplum Deī quisque est in imāgine parvā' cujus cāsūs est nōmen 'exemplum'?"**

   a) **" 'Exemplum' est cāsūs _____ ."**

b) " 'Quisque' est cāsūs _____ ."

c) " 'Deī' est cāsūs _____ ."

4) Questions on new Basic Sentences:
   a) **"Quō membrō malī servī laeditur dominus?"**

     " _____ ."

   b) **"Quae animālia morte lupī adjuvantur?"**

     " _____ ."

5) What Basic Sentence in this Unit expresses approximately this thought?
Artēs animum hominis faciunt.
Ōrā - - -   cul - - -   ani - -   - - t.

_____ .

6) Write the new Basic Sentence which this picture illustrates:
Glō - - -   umb - -   virt - - - -   - - t.

_____ .

7) What review Basic Sentence expresses approximately this thought?
Juvenēs formā, nōn animō, in amōre dūcuntur.
Oc - - -   sunt   in   amō - -   duc - -.

_____ .

8) Write the review Basic Sentences which these pictures illustrate:
   a) **Asin - -   as - - - ,   s - -   s - -   pul - - - -.**

_____ .

b) **Nē · · līb · · · · t quī corp · · · ser · · · ·**

_____

_____ .

c) **R · · nōn sp · ·, fac · · · · · · dic · · ·,
quae · · · amīc · · ·**

_____

_____ .

EXTRA READINGS
Underlined words are those which have not yet appeared in _Latin: Level One._

a) **Timor Dominī fōns vītae.** Motto

_____

_____ .

b) **Imāgō animī vultus; indicēs oculī.** Cicero, _Dē Or,_ 3.59.221

_____

_____ .

TEST FOR UNIT 23 OF *LATIN: LEVEL ONE*

1) Answer the questions on the pictures:

a) **"Quōrum aurēs longae sunt?"** **"_____."**

b) **"Quōrum pedēs parvī sunt?"** **"_____."**

c) **"Quōrum dicta acerba sunt?"** **"_____."**

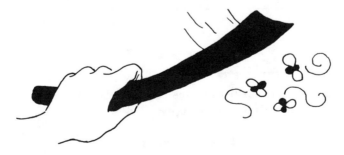

d) **"Quōrum vīta brevis est?"** **"_____."**

2) Write the complete paradigm, singular and plural, of the following nouns:

a) **puella** _____ _____   b) **equus** _____ _____

_____ _____   _____ _____

_____ _____   _____ _____

_____ _____   _____ _____

_____ _____   _____ _____

c) **fātum** _____ _____   d) **rēx** _____ _____

_____ _____   _____ _____

_____ _____   _____ _____

_____ _____   _____ _____

_____ _____   _____ _____

e) **genus** _____ _____   f) **quercus** _____ _____

_____ _____   _____ _____

_____ _____   _____ _____

_____ _____   _____ _____

_____ _____   _____ _____

g) **rēs** _____ _____

_____ _____

_____ _____

_____ _____

_____ _____

3) Answer these questions on the new Basic Sentences:
Gravis īra rēgum est semper.

a) **"Quī, sī īrātī sunt, inopēs laedunt?"**

"_____."

Latin: Level One Test for Unit Twenty-three/80

Rērum hūmānārum domina Fortūna.

b) "Ā quō hominēs reguntur?"

    "Ā _____ ."

4) Write the new Basic Sentences which these pictures illustrate:
Nē ·· mort ····· omn ···· hōr ·· s ··· t.

_____

_____ .

Vī ·· mortu ···· in mem ···· vīv ···· e ··
pos ···· .

_____

_____

_____ .

5) Answer this question on a review Basic Sentence:
Plōrātur lacrimīs āmissa pecūnia vērīs.
"Quālēs sunt lacrimae cum pecūnia āmissa est?"

    "_____ ."

6) Write the review Basic Sentences which these pictures illustrate:
   N - - cēn - s - - e ap - - n - - - er, T - - -,
      Caecili - - - -.
      Bell - - conv - - - - C - - - - - - - - - s hab - - -.

   _____

   _____

   _____.

Nāv - - qu - - - - flū - - - - mag - - - - t in m - - -
parv - - - - - t.

   _____

   _____.

Q - - ping - - flōr - - fl - - - - n - - p - - - - t
odō - - - -.

   _____

   _____.

EXTRA READINGS

a) **Patria commūnis est omnium parēns.** Cicero, *Cat.*
1.7.17

_____

_____ .

b) **Quī ēbrium lūdificat, laedit absentem.** Anon.

_____

_____

_____ .

TEST FOR UNIT 24 OF *LATIN: LEVEL ONE*

1) Write the singular paradigm of **timēre.**

    1st person   _____

    2d person   _____

    3d person   _____

2) Expand with the pronoun which can be the subject of the verb.

    a) _____ **beneficium dās.**

    b) _____ **omnibus miserīs noceō.**

    c) _____ **nōn cēnās sine aprō.**

    d) _____ **levēs capiō animōs.**

3) Give the various forms as required:

    a) **"Quid est 'difficultās' in cāsū datīvō et numerō singulārī?" "_____."**

    b) **"Quid est 'flōs' in cāsū accūsātīvō et numerō plūrālī?" "_____."**

    c) **"Quid est 'effigiēs' in cāsū genitīvō et numerō singulārī?" "_____."**

    d) **"Quid est 'arcus' in cāsū datīvō et numerō singulārī?" "_____."**

    e) **"Quid est 'caelum' in cāsū accūsātīvō et numerō singulārī?" "_____."**

    f) **"Quid est 'vestis' in cāsū ablātīvō et numerō singulārī?" "_____."**

    g) **"Quid est 'diēs' in cāsū nōminātīvō et numerō plūrālī?" "_____."**

h) "Quid est 'rāna' in cāsū datīvō et numerō

   plūrālī?" "_____."

i) "Quid est 'flūmen' in cāsū genitīvō et numerō

   plūrālī?" "_____."

j) "Quid est 'dominus' in cāsū ablātīvō et numerō

   plūrālī?" "_____."

4) Answer these questions on new Basic Sentences:
   Omnia mors poscit; lēx est, nōn poena, perīre.

   a) "Quāliter omnēs pereunt?"
      "J - - - -."

      "_____."

   Nātūram quidem mūtāre difficile est.

   b) "Quantōs saltūs nōn facit nātūra?"

      "_____."

5) Write the new Basic Sentence which expresses approximately
   this thought:
   **Ille nōn est philosophus vērus, etiam sī aspectū suō
   philosophō similis est.**
   Vid - - bar - - - et pal - - - - ; philos - - - - -
   nōn - - - v - - - - .

   _____

   _____ .

6) Write the new Basic Sentence which this picture illustrates:
   Aur - - - - ten - - lup - - .

Latin: Level One Test for Unit Twenty-four/86

7) Say that it is easy to do these things:
   a) **Vēritātem diēs aperit.** ⟶
     Facil· ··t v········ ap·····.

     _____ .

   b) **Auctor opus laudat.** ⟶
     F····· ··t op·· l·······.

     _____ .

8) Write the review Basic Sentence which expresses approximately this thought:
Sapiēns nihil, etiam in rēbus bonīs, nimis agit.
Imp···· f···· s······ et r···· h·······.

     _____

     _____ .

9) Write the review Basic Sentences which these pictures illustrate:
   a) **Glō··· um··· virt···· ··t.**

     _____

     _____ .

   b) **Vī·· vīn·· ··t.**

     _____

     _____ .

c) **For·· bo··· frag··· ··t.**

_____

_____.

EXTRA READINGS

a) **Multōs timēre dēbet quem multī timent.** Publilius
Syrus

_____

_____.

b) **Saepe creat mollēs aspera spīna rosās.** Med.

_____

_____.

TEST FOR UNIT 25 OF *LATIN: LEVEL ONE*

1) Write the paradigms of the following verbs:

    a)   **stāre**   b)   **vidēre**

    _____   _____   _____   _____

    _____   _____   _____   _____

    _____   _____   _____   _____

    c)   **petere**   d)   **aspicere (-iō)**

    _____   _____   _____   _____

    _____   _____   _____   _____

    _____   _____   _____   _____

    e)   **custōdīre**

    _____   _____

    _____   _____

    _____   _____

2) a) **"Quid est 'necessitās' in cāsū datīvō et numerō singulārī?"** **"_____."**

    b) **"Quid est 'dolor' in cāsū genitīvō et numerī plūrālī?"** **"_____."**

    c) **"Quid est 'poena' in cāsū accūsātīvō et numerō singulārī?"** **"_____."**

    d) **"Quid est 'nōmen' in cāsū accūsātīvō et numerō singulārī?"** **"_____."**

    e) **"Quid est 'vōx' in cāsū genitīvō et numerō plūrālī?"** **"_____."**

3) a) Call **Caeciliānus**, using the special calling

form: "_____."

b) Call **Sabidius,** using the special calling

form: "_____."

4) Answer this question on a new Basic Sentence:
"Capere cōnsilium potes; quantus est dolor tuus?"

"___L_____."

5) Write the new Basic Sentence which this picture illustrates:
Hōr - - n - - num - - -, n - - ī serē - - - .

_____

_____.

6) Answer this question on a review Basic Sentence:
Nēmō mortālium omnibus hōrīs sapit.
"Quid tū nōn semper agis?"

"Egō nōn semper _____."

7) Write the review Basic Sentences which these pictures illustrate:
a) **M - - ō in c - - - - - - ō fēm - - - - vinc - - - vir - - .**

_____

_____.

b) **M - - s īnf - - - - fēl - -, juv - - - acer - -,**
   n - - - s sēr - sen - .

_____

_____ .

c) **Mo - - lu - - agn - - vī - - .**

_____ .

EXTRA READINGS

a) **Praeterita mūtāre nōn possumus.** Anon.

_____

_____ .

b) **Effugere cupiditātem rēgnum est vincere.** Publilius
Syrus

_____

_____ .

TEST FOR UNIT 26 OF *LATIN: LEVEL ONE*

1) a) Write the #1 forms of **cēnāre**:

        _____   _____

        _____   _____

        _____   _____

   b) Write the #2 forms of **regere**:

        _____   _____

        _____   _____

        _____   _____

   c) Write the #3 forms of **lavāre**:

        _____   _____

        _____   _____

        _____   _____

   d) Write the #3 forms of **premere**:

        _____   _____

        _____   _____

        _____   _____

2) Identify by number (#1, #2, or #3) the tense of the following verb forms which you have not seen before.

   a) **saliēmus** _____   b) **quiēscētis** _____

   c) **effugiet** _____   d) **laudant** _____

   e) **plōrābō** _____   f) **timēs** _____

   g) **poscō** _____   h) **dēbēmus** _____

   i) **sentiēs** _____

3) a) "Quid est 'tempus' in cāsū genitīvō et

numerō singulārī?" "_____."

b) "Quid est 'lingua' in cāsū accūsatīvō et

numerō plūrālī?" "_____."

c) "Quid est 'quercus' in cāsū genitīvō et

numerō plūrālī?" "_____."

d) "Quid est 'faciēs' in cāsū accūsātīvō et

numerō singulārī?" "_____."

e) "Quid est 'verbum' in cāsū accūsātīvō et

numerō plūrālī?" "_____."

f) "Quid est 'equus' in cāsū genitīvō et

numerō singulārī?" "_____."

4) Give the synopses (forms #1, #2, and #3) of the following
verbs in the person and number indicated:

a) **manēre,** 2d singular (**tū** as subject)

#1 _____

#2 _____

#3 _____

b) **obumbrāre**, 1st singular (**egō** as subject)

#1 _____

#2 _____

#3 _____

c) **effugere** (**-iō**), 2d plural (**vōs** as subject)

#1 _____

#2 _____

#3 _____

d) **custōdīre**, 2d singular (**tū** as subject)

#1 _____

#2 _____

#3 _____

5) Answer these questions on these new Basic Sentences:

a) **Quid nōbīs omnibus accidet?"**

" **M**   ."

b) **Orbem jam tōtum victor Rōmānus habēbat.**
   "Quem metuēbat tōtus orbis terrārum?"

"_____ _____."

6) Write the new Basic Sentence which this picture illustrates:
   S - -   qu - -   custōd - - -   ips - -   c - - - - - s?

_____

_____ ?

7) Answer this question on a review Basic Sentence:
   Nātūram quidem mūtāre difficile est.
   "Quantā difficultāte mūtātur nātūra?"

"_____."

8) Write the review Basic Sentence which the picture illustrates:
Cae-- duc-- quaer---; n-s s--e du-- err-----.

_____

_____.

EXTRA READINGS

a) **Crūdēlitātis māter est avāritia.** Quintilian 9.3.89

_____

_____.

b) **Iu magnō grandēs capiuntur flūmine piscēs.** Med.

_____

_____.

1) a) **"Quō locō puella stat?"**
   "Tr - - - - - - - - - - ."

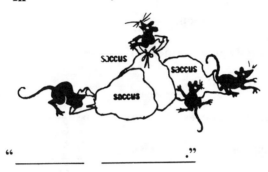

flūmen

"_____ _____ ."

b) **"Quō locō sunt mūrēs?"**
   "In - - - - - - - - - ."

saccus

saccus

saccus

saccus

"_____ _____ ."

2) Write the paradigm of the #5 form of **capiō, capere, cēpī, captus**:

_____ _____

_____ _____

_____ _____

Here are sentences which contain #5 forms of verbs which you have not seen but whose #2 forms you do know. Transform these #5 verbs to the #2 form in the same number and person.

Example: **Tū omnia poposcistī.** ⟶ **Tu omnia poscis.**

a) **Canis aprum momordit.** ⟶

   Canis aprum _____ .

b) **Egō vēritātem quaesīvī.** ⟶

   Egō vēritātem _____ .

Latin: Level One Test for Unit Twenty-seven/97

c)   Tū lupum īrātum aspexistī. ———→

Tū lupum īrātum _____ .

d)   Hominēs hōrās serēnās numerāvērunt. ———→

Hominēs hōrās serēnās _____ .

e)   Hominī jūstō nocuimus. ———→

Hominī jūstō _____ .

f)   Pedem gradibus imposuī. ———→

Pedem gradibus _____ .

g)   Certās rēs saepe mīsistis. ———→

Certās rēs saepe _____ .

h)   Agnī lupum timuērunt. ———→

Agnī lupum _____ .

i)   Magnās litterās in gradū scrīpsī. ———→

Magnās litterās in gradū _____ .

j)   Equum ad lacum dūxistī. ———→

Equum ad lacum _____ .

4)   Write the principal parts of these verbs:

a)   **eō,** _____ , _____ .

b)   **lūdō,** _____ , _____ , _____ .

c)   **edō,** _____ , _____ , _____ .

d)   **currō,** _____ , _____ _____ .

e)   **videō,** _____ , _____ , _____ .

5)   Give the noun forms asked for:

a)   **"Quid est 'sīdus' in cāsū ablātīvō et numerō plūrālī?"**

"_____ ."

b) **"Quid est 'fidēs' in cāsū datīvō**

   et numerō singulārī?" "_____."

c) **"Quid est 'cursus' in cāsū ablātīvō**

   et numerō singulārī?" "_____."

d) **"Quid est 'certāmen' in cāsū ablātīvō et**

   numerō singulārī?" "_____."

6) Write the new Basic Sentences which these pictures illustrate:
   a) **N - x er - -, et cae - - fulg - - - - l - - - ser - - -**
      in - - - min - - - sīd - - - -.

_____

_____.

b) **Lūs - - - - s - - - s, ēd - - - - sat - - at - - -**
      bib - - - -;
      t - - - - s ab - - - t - - i - - t.

_____

_____

_____.

c) **Dīv··· nāt··· de··· ag···; a·· hūm···
aedif······ urb···.**

_____

_____ .

7) Write the review Basic Sentences which express approximately
these thoughts:

Sī deōs colimus, rem pūblicam custōdīmus.

a) **Rel···· v··a ··· firm······· r··
pūbl····.**

_____

_____ .

Rēgēs omnia vident atque audiunt.

b) **Mult·· r···m aur·· atq·· oc····.**

_____

_____ .

EXTRA READINGS

a) **Sūmere vult piscēs cattus sed flūmen abhorret.** Med.

_____

_____ .

b) **Mē lūmen, vōs umbra regit.** Sundial inscription

_____

_____ .

TEST FOR UNIT 28 OF *LATIN: LEVEL ONE*

1) Count from one to ten; remember the agreement of the adjective   2 points each word.
    in the first three.

a) _____ **digitus**

b) _____ **digitī**

c) _____ **digitī**

d) _____ **digitī**

e) _____ **digitī**

f) _____ **digitī**

g) _____ **digitī**

h) _____ **digitī**

i) _____ digitī

j. _____ digitī

2) Write the principal parts of the following verbs:

   a) **trahō,** _____ , _____ , _____ .

   b) **aperiō,** _____ , _____ , _____ .

   c) **quaerō,** _____ , _____ , _____ .

   d) **maneō,** _____ , _____ .

3) Write the conjugation of **laedō, laedere, laesī, laesus** in the #4 tense:

   _____ _____

   _____ _____

   _____ _____

4) Identify the tenses of the verbs in these changed Basic Sentences (**prīmī/secundī/tertiī/quārtī/quīntī**):

   In ūnō saltū lepidē aprōs cēpī duōs.

   a) " 'Cēpī' est temporis _____ ."

   Certa mittēmus dum incerta petimus.

   b) " 'Mittēmus' est temporis _____ ."

   Caelō fulget lūna serēnō inter minōra sīdera.

   c) " 'Fulget' est temporis _____ ."

5) Write the following noun forms:
   a) **"Quid est 'lepus' in cāsū ablātīvō et numerō**

   plūrālī?" " _____ .**"**

b) **"Quid est 'lūx' in cāsū ablātīvō et numerō singulārī?"** **"_____."**

c) **"Quid est 'pictūra' in cāsū genitīvō et numerō plūrālī?"** **"_____."**

d) **"Quid est 'aciēs' in cāsū ablātīvō et numerō singulārī?"** **"_____."**

e) **"Quid est 'manus' in cāsū accūsātīvō et numerō plūrālī?"** **"_____."**

6) Give the new Basic Sentence which expresses approximately this thought:
Hodiē nōs omnēs vitia habēmus.
Qu·· fu····· vit··, mōr·· s····.

_____.

7) Fill in the missing letters:

La __ __ __ ēbam, sed tū comit __ __ __ __ prōtin __ __

ad m __

vēn __ __ __, cent __ __, Symmach __,

dis __ __ __ ulīs.

C __ __ __ um mē tetig __ __ __ man __ __ Aquil __ __ __

gelātae.

Nōn hab __ __ fēbr __ __, Symmache, n __ __ c

hab __ __.

8) Review Basic Sentence:
Hōrās nōn numerō, nisī serēnās.
"Quālia tempora tū in memoriā tenēre dēbēs?"

"Egō tempora _____ in memoriā tenēre

_____."

EXTRA READINGS

a) **Quī amat mē, amat et canem meum.** Anon.

_____

_____ .

b) **Dūcit amor patriae.** Motto of Lord Milford

_____

_____ .

TEST FOR UNIT 29 OF *LATIN: LEVEL ONE*

1) Write the synopses of the following verbs:

    a) **habeō, habēre, habuī, habitus** in the 2d singular (**Tū** as subject):

        #1 _____ #2 _____ #3 _____

        #4 _____ #5 _____ #6 _____

    b) **stō, stāre, stetī** in the 3d plural (**Virī** as subject):

        #1 _____ #2 _____ #3 _____

        #4 _____ #5 _____ #6 _____

2) Give the principal parts of the following verbs:

    a) **faciō,** _____ , _____ , _____ .

    b) **pōnō,** _____ , _____ , _____ .

    c) **tendō,** _____ , _____ , _____ .

    d) **rumpō,** _____ , _____ , _____ .

    e) **fugiō,** _____ , _____ .

3) Conjugate the irregular verb **volō** in the #2 tense:

    _____ _____

    _____ _____

    _____ _____

4) a) **"Quid est 'aedificium' in cāsū accūsātīvō et numerō plūrālī?" "** _____ **."**

    b) **"Quid est 'hospes' in cāsū genitīvō et numerō singulārī?" "** _____ **."**

    c) **"Quid est 'carmen' in cāsū ablātīvō et numerō singulārī?" "** _____ **."**

d) **"Quid est 'sinus' in cāsū ablātīvō et**

numerō singulārī?" "_____."

e) **"Quid est 'libellus' in cāsū ablātīvō et**

numerō plūrālī?" "____ _____."

5) Write the Basic Sentence which this picture illustrates:
Dōn - - er - - fē - - x, mul - - - numer - - - -
  amī - - - ;
  temp - - - sī f - - - - nt nūb - - -, sōl - - er - - .

_____

_____

_____ .

6) Answer these questions on one of the new Readings:
   a) **"Quem auctōrem omnēs Rōmānī laudābant?"**

   " ____**M**_____ ."

   b) **Quid agēbat quīdam cui carmina Mārtiālis
   nōn placēbant?"**

   "**R**_____ , **p**_____ , **st**_____ ,

   ō_____ , **ōsc**_____ ."
   (Two verbs are enough.)

7) Complete the blanks on this new Reading:

   Ho __ es erās nost __ sem __ r, Matho,
   Tīb __ tīnī.

   Hocc em __ . Imp __ uī; r __ t __ i
   vendo tuum.

8) Answer this question on a review Basic Sentence:
    Vēritās vōs līberābit.
    "Quālēs erimus sī vēritātem colimus?"

    " **L**   ."

9) Complete the blanks in the review Reading:

    Nūp __ **er** _ _ **medic** _ _ **, n** _ _ **c est**

    vespillo   Diaul _ _

    _ _ **od   v** _ _ _ _ _ **fac** _ _ **, f** _ _ **erat   et**

    medicus.

EXTRA READINGS

a) **Glōriam quī sprēverit, vēram habēbit.** Livy 22.39.20

    _____

    _____.

b) **Cum fortūna perit, nūllus amīcus erit.** Med.

    _____

    _____.

TEST FOR UNIT 30 OF *LATIN: LEVEL ONE*

1) Here is a verb meaning "be on fire": **ardeō, ardēre, arsī.** Give a synopsis in the 2d person plural (**Vōs** as subject):

   #1 _____   #2 _____   #3 _____

   #4 _____   #5 _____   #6 _____

2) Give the principal parts of the following verbs:

   a) **vincō,** _____ , _____ , _____ .

   b) **capiō,** _____ , _____ , _____ .

   c) **laxō,** _____ , _____ , _____ .

   d) **pingō,** _____ , _____ , _____ .

   e) **adjuvō,** _____ , _____ , _____ .

3) a) **"Quid est 'successus' in cāsū genitīvō et numerō singulārī?" "** _____ **."**

   b) **"Quid est 'gena' in cāsū nōminātīvō et numerō plūrālī?" "** _____ **."**

   c) **"Quid est 'color' in cāsū datīvō et numerō singulārī?" "** _____ **."**

   d) **"Quid est 'somnus' in cāsū ablātīvō et numerō singulārī?" "** _____ **."**

   e) **"Quid est 'ōs' in cāsū accūsātīvō et numerō singulārī?" "** _____ **."**

4) Fill in the blanks on this new Reading:

   Qu _ _ recitās, m _ _ _ est, Ō Fīdentīn _ ,

       lib _ _ lus;

     sed ma _ _ cum r _ _ _ _ _ , incip _ _ e _ _ e

   tuus.

5) **Lōtus nōbīscum est, hilaris cēnāvit, et īdem
inventus māne est mortuus Andragorās.
Tam subitae mortis causam, Faustīne, requīris?
In somnīs medicum vīderat Hermocratēn.**

(Reading #12)

Answer these questions on the new Reading:
a) **"Quāliter cēnāvit Andragorās?"**

"_____."

b) **"Quis quaerit, 'Cūr haec mors accidit?'?"**

"_____."

c) **"Quālis erat mors Andragorae?"**

"_____."

d) **"Cujus amīcus erat Andragorās?"**

"_____."

6) Fill in the blanks on this Review Reading:

Si qu _ _ ō le _ _ _ em mi _ _ is, mihi,

Gellia, dīc _ _ ,

"F _ _ _ ōsus septem, M _ _ _ e , d _ _ bus

e _ _ ₃."

Sī nōn dēr _ _ ēs, sī vēr _ _ , l _ _ mea,

nār _ _ _

_ _ istī numq _ _ _ , Gelli _ , tū

lepo _ _ _ .

7) Write the review Basic Sentences which these pictures illustrate:
a) **- - od n - - ded - - For - - - - n - - ēri - - - .**

Latin: Level One Test for Unit Thirty/110

b) **Lin - - a   m - - ī   p - - s   pes - - - -   ser - - -**

_____ .

c) **J - - que   quiēsc - - - - -   vō - - -   hom - - - - - - -**
      can - - - - -
    l - - - que   noct - - - - -   al - -   reg - - - -   eq - - - -

_____

_____ .

EXTRA READINGS

a) **In idem flūmen bis dēscendimus et nōn
dēscendimus. Manet enim idem flūminis nōmen;
aqua trānsmissa est.** Seneca, _Ep._ 58.23

_____

_____

_____

_____ .

b) **Bis vincit quī sē vincit in victōriā.** Publilius Syrus

_____

_____ .

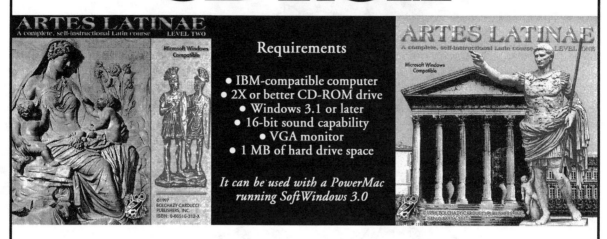